Adult Christmas Activity Book

Mixed Activities about Christmas including Sudokus, Crosswords, Wordsearches, Riddles, and More

by JEST FEST

The INNARDS

PART 1 - THE CHRISTMAS STORY

PART 2 - CHRISTMAS TIME

PART 3 – The ANSWERS

BONUS CHRISTMAS BADGE

MORE FROM JEST FEST

EXTRAORDINARY CHRISTMASES

This paperback first edition first published in 2022 by Dialog Abroad Books

2 4 6 8 10 9 7 5 3 1

ISBN: 978-3-948706-85-2

PART 1

THE CHRISTMAS STORY

With the gathering of loved ones and the giving of presents, people sometimes forget that Christmas is a celebration of the birth of our lord Jesus Christ.

This book begins with a gentle retelling of the story of the birth of Jesus. Then it's time to grab a pen and see how well you remember the first ever Christmas with various word puzzles, fun activities, and brainteasers.

The Story of the Birth of Jesus

A long time ago, in a place called Nazareth, lived a woman called Mary. She was a hardworking woman who always treated others well. She was engaged to be married to a man called Joseph, who was also good at heart.

One day, God sent an angel by the name of Gabriel to Mary. The angel told Mary that God was sending a holy spirit to Earth to be the savior of the world. That soul would be born as Mary's son, and she would name him Jesus.

Mary was worried about how this was possible since she wasn't yet married to Joseph, but the angel assured her that it would be a miracle from God. The angel also told Mary that her cousin, Elizabeth, who had no children, would also give birth to a baby called John. John's birth would prepare the way for Jesus' birth.

When she heard this, Mary consented to God's will. She went to see Elizabeth and returned after three months. By this time, she was pregnant. Joseph was worried and wondered if he should go ahead with the wedding. But one night, while he was asleep, the angel visited Joseph and told him about God's will and urged him to marry Mary. The angel also told Joseph that the child should be called Jesus. Joseph woke up the next morning and decided that he would make Mary his wife.

After the wedding, Joseph and Mary were forced to make a trip to Bethlehem, the place where Joseph's family came from, to participate in a census and satisfy an imperial command from the Roman emperor. However, when they reached there, they could not find a place to stay as the town was so crowded. With little choice, they had to stay in a barn where animals lived. It was there that Mary gave birth to the Son of God, Jesus Christ.

The birth of Jesus was signified by a bright star in the sky. Wise men from different parts of the world quickly understood the significance of this star and followed it to reach Bethlehem. They brought along gifts for the baby. In other parts of Bethlehem, where shepherds were grazing their sheep, angels appeared to give them the good news. They sang and made merry to welcome the Holy Spirit to earth.

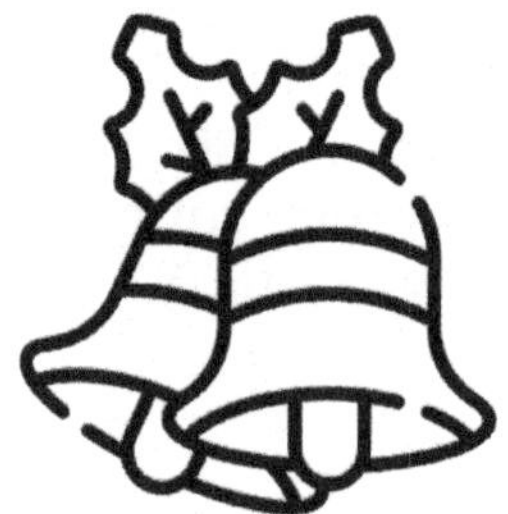

Since then, this day has been celebrated as Christmas. People go to church at midnight to celebrate the birth of Jesus Christ. They exchange gifts, sing carols, and enjoy themselves.

Mary and Joseph Meet

Mary and Joseph want to meet but are moving in opposite directions around the town. Mary moves two places counterclockwise at each stage and Joseph moves one place clockwise at each stage. After how many stages will they be together in the same corner of town?

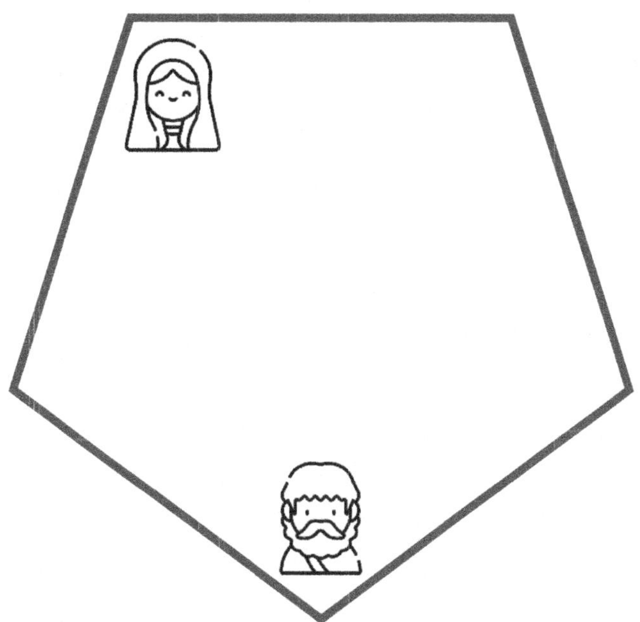

Select an answer:
A: 3 Stages
B: 4 Stages
C: 5 Stages
D: 6 Stages

Noel Number Puzzle Picture

In any order you wish, copy the contents of each square in the jumbled picture below to the same numbered square in the blank grid on the next page until the entire puzzle is done, then add vivid shades to your masterpiece.

41	53	3	16	48	37	47	2
54	5	29	25	61	4	14	44
24	10	0	19	20	8	18	55
12	30	51	27	22	23	45	43
32	59	15	58	36	40	49	13
34	62	6	35	38	46	9	52
28	63	33	26	1	60	39	7
56	57	42	11	31	17	50	21

0	1	2	3	4	5	6	7
8	9	10	11	12	13	14	15
16	17	18	19	20	21	22	23
24	25	26	27	28	29	30	31
32	33	34	35	36	37	38	39
40	41	42	43	44	45	46	47
48	49	50	51	52	53	54	55
56	57	58	59	60	61	62	63

Carol Search

The titles of six traditional carols based on the Nativity are hidden below. Can you find and circle them?

M	X	B	V	J	H	W	Y	J	Q	C	M	U	T	V
C	C	G	L	U	P	H	B	O	G	F	X	G	N	Z
F	S	J	I	F	M	A	Y	H	B	Y	F	N	M	T
C	W	P	E	Z	Z	T	A	O	N	O	O	Q	Z	H
O	E	L	Y	A	Z	C	B	L	F	C	S	A	E	G
P	T	W	W	H	V	H	U	Y	O	B	E	F	F	I
M	H	V	N	L	H	I	Y	N	S	W	D	J	G	N
X	R	V	X	I	D	L	E	I	K	R	W	G	R	T
P	E	V	T	I	Z	D	O	G	D	E	A	F	J	N
F	E	I	R	P	T	I	P	H	G	A	M	A	L	E
B	K	C	N	L	J	S	P	T	E	N	V	U	L	L
M	I	E	I	V	I	T	Y	Q	W	T	M	A	C	I
D	N	J	N	T	K	H	R	K	M	W	C	Z	O	S
F	G	D	A	Y	N	I	H	M	Y	Z	Q	B	C	H
Y	S	G	H	D	U	S	K	G	J	Y	G	V	T	Z
F	R	E	G	N	A	M	A	N	I	Y	A	W	A	Q
V	P	H	O	S	B	W	T	J	Z	A	L	W	A	M
A	E	G	L	O	R	A	C	O	S	P	Y	L	A	C

Starring Role Riddler

Rearrange these phrases to reveal some unforgettable people from the Nativity story.

Faze no, just share

Answer: ______________________________

Brighten mass delivery

Answer: ______________________________

The red-hot rage

Answer: ______________________________

Rut cause us saga

Answer: ______________________________

Ruthless Sudoku

Fill in the blank squares so that each row, each column, and each 3-by-3 block contain the letters C, D, E, H, J, O, R, S, U.

The letters you produce from the highlighted squares completes the following phrase:

"I, King ______________ ordered all the male children under two years in Bethlehem to be killed in my attempt to get rid of the baby Jesus."

D		C	R				S	
		H		J		C		O
E							H	
O			E	S				C
			D		U			
U				R	C			D
	C							S
R		S		U		H		
	E				S	J		U

Turn to page 39

Wise Letters

Test your creative thinking skills with these challenging letter puzzles.

1. Which letter is three to the right of the letter immediately to the left of the letter that is four to the left of the letter O?

M E L C H I O R

2. I am a 9-letter wise man.
9, 2, 7, 5 = being hasty
7, 6, 3, 4 = an essential seasoning
1, 8, 4 = used to hit baseballs
Who am I?

= ______________

3. What letter should replace the question mark in this star?

Chronicle Crossword

Test your knowledge of the Christmas story. Hint: Some answers can be found at the start of this book.

1. **The gift given to Jesus by Gaspar.**
2. **The gift given to Jesus by Balthasar.**
3. **Where baby Jesus lay in the barn.**
4. **Father Joseph's occupation.**
5. **The Nativity accounts appear in the Gospels of Matthew and ______.**
6. **The town where Mary lived.**
7. **The wise men followed this to Bethlehem.**
8. **The title that served as a description of Jesus' role as the Messiah as "God with us".**
9. **The gift given to Jesus by Melchior.**
10. **The name of Mary's cousin.**
11. **The three wise men are collectively known as the ______.**
12. **The name of the angle that spoke to Mary.**

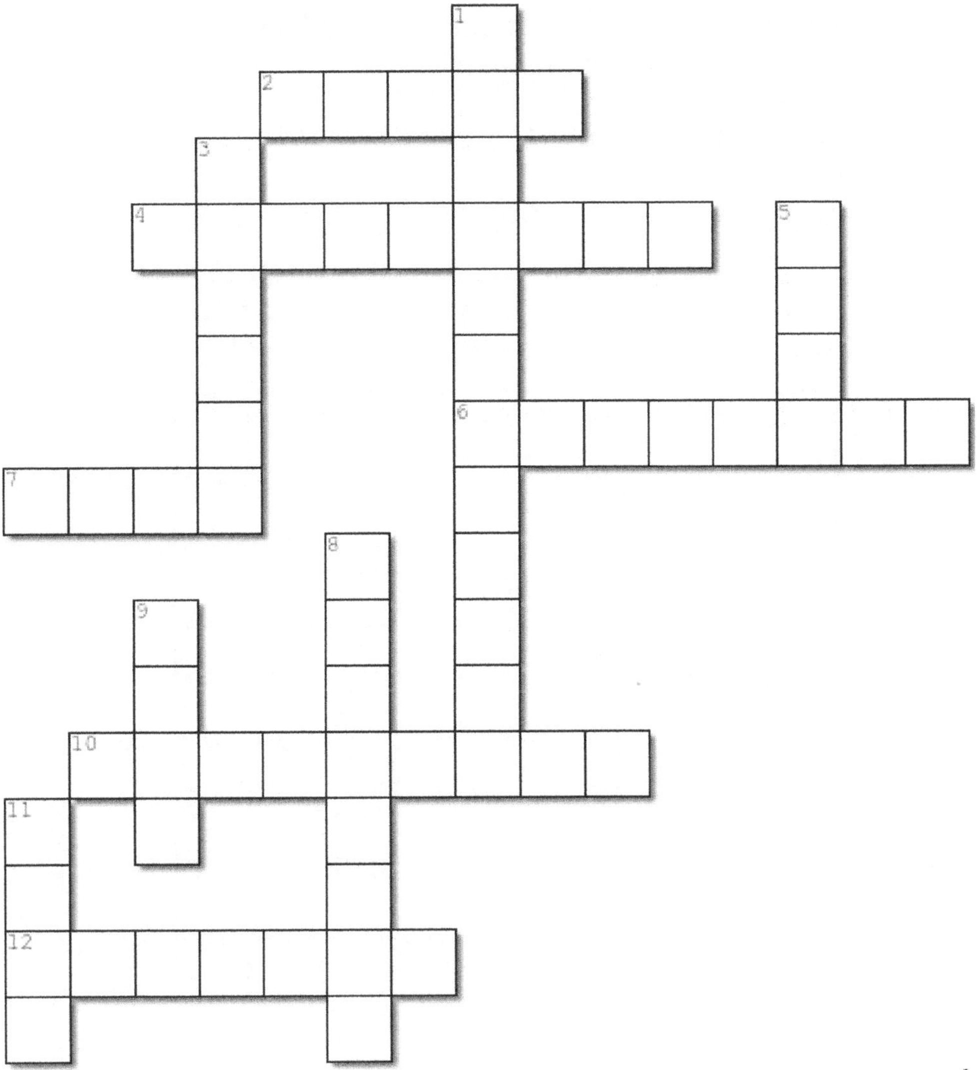

1
2
3
4
5
6
7
8
9
10
11
12

Star Sudoku

Fill in the blank squares so that each row, each column, and each 3-by-3 block contain the letters A, D, E, G, N, O, S, T, V.

The letters you produce from the highlighted squares completes the following phrase:

"_______________ is the season of reflection and preparation for the birth of Jesus Christ."

	E				T			
N		O	S					
	S	A		G			O	
		G			O	A		
				S	G	O	V	N
		N			D	S		
	A	T		D			E	
G		S	E					
	V				S			

Connect the Dots

Connect the dots to reveal the picture. Use the numbers to guide you. When you land on a dot with a circle around it, take your pen off and start again at the next number with a star.

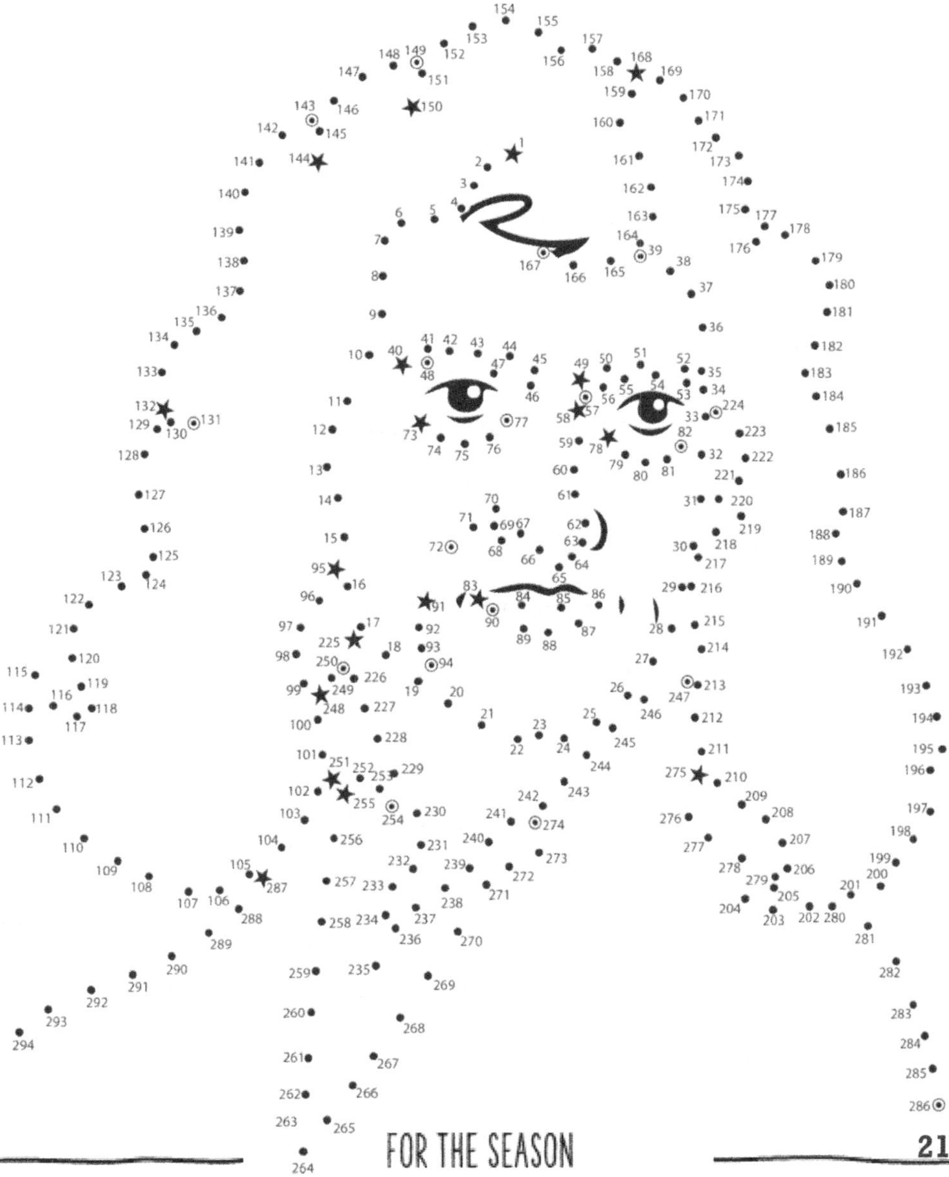

Complete the Carol Lyrics

Nothing beats singing traditional hymns at Christmas time. Fill in the blanks below with the correct lyrics and prove yourself a Christmas carol expert.

"O come, all ye faithful, joyful and ___________,
Come ye, O come ye, to Bethlehem.
Come and _______ Him, born the _____ of angels"

"___________, go where I send thee
How shall I send thee?
I'm gonna send thee one by one
One for the little _______ baby
That was born, born
Born in ___________"

"Joy to the world! the Lord is come
Let _______ receive her ______
Let every heart prepare Him room,
and ________ and nature ______"

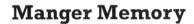

Manger Memory

Let's put your memory to the test. Which of the following four images matches exactly with the nativity scene image at the start of this book?

Note Space

Use these pages if you need to jot something down when solving the puzzles and riddles in this section.

Turn to page 72

PART 2

CHRISTMAS TIME

Although it's important to always bring to mind the time when Jesus was born, the world 2000 years ago was a very different place than it is today.

Christmas nowadays is about decorations, presents under the tree, family gatherings, and Christmas movies on TV. With pen still in hand, it's time to enjoy some fantastically festive activities about Christmas.

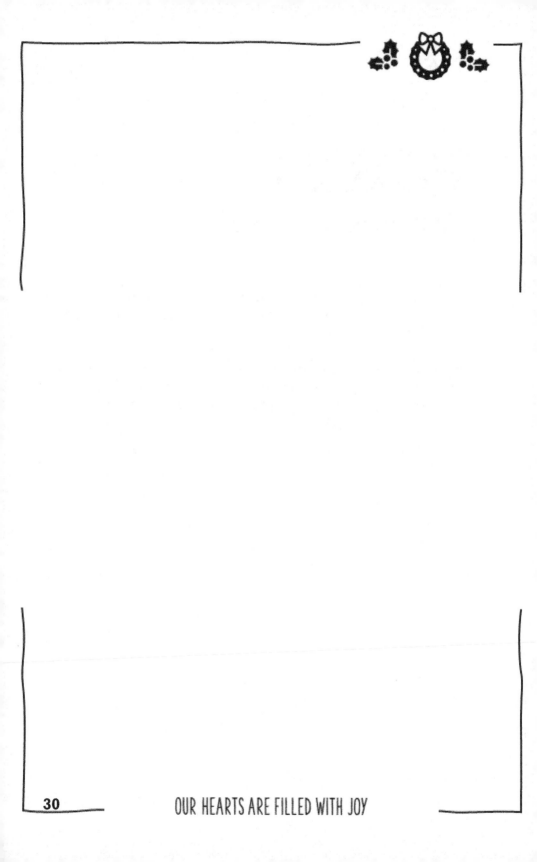

How Many Can You Spot?

How many candy canes are in this picture? ________

Complete the Lyrics

The following lyrics were taken from classic Christmas songs you no doubt love listening to year after year. But your help is needed to fill in the missing words.

"It's the most wonderful time of the year
With the kids ________ _________
And everyone telling you be of ______ cheer
It's the most wonderful time of the year"

"Jingle bell, jingle bell, jingle bell ______
Jingle bells swing and jingle bells ring
_________ and _________ up bushels of fun
Now the jingle _____ has begun"

"I'm ___________ of a white Christmas
Just like the ______ I used to know
Where the treetops _________
And children listen
To hear _______ ______ in the snow"

"________' around the Christmas tree
At the Christmas ______ hop
__________ hung where you can see
Every ______ tries to stop"

"I saw Mommy ________ Santa Claus
____________ the mistletoe last night
She didn't see me _____
Down the stairs to have a _____"

"Have yourself a merry _____ Christmas
Let your _____ be light
From now on your ______ will be out of _____"

"I don't want a _____ for Christmas
There is just one _____ I need
I don't _____ about the ________ underneath
the Christmas tree"

The Twelve Days Crossword

Test your knowledge of 'The Twelve Days of Christmas' – the classic, singalong Christmas carol that runs through the twelve days that make up the Christmas season from Christmas Day and to 6 January, the day before Epiphany.

1. **The number of gold rings.**
2. **Nine ladies are doing this.**
3. **How many pipers are piping?**
4. **Ten lords are ...**
5. **There are only two of these.**
6. **What number of maids are a-milking?**
7. **Four birds are doing this.**
8. **What is in a pear tree?**
9. **What are six geese up to?**
10. **Where do the three hens come from?**
11. **Swans are a-swimming, but how many?**
12. **How many drummers are drumming?**

1
2
3
4
5
6
7
8
9
10
11
12

Delicious Dessert

Nothing brings back memories like the sweets of a childhood Christmas. See if you can guess the popular Yuletide dessert from just the ingredients below...without feeling hungry!

Eggs
Golden caster sugar
Plain flour
Cocoa powder
Baking powder
Butter
Dark chocolate
Golden syrup
Double cream
Icing sugar
Holly sprigs to decorate

Answer: ______________________________

CLUE: This dessert is best suited to be eaten by the fireplace. The filling sometimes includes crushed mints, but it's the original that will surely take your tastebuds on a trip down memory lane.

Name the Movie 1

Guess the classic Christmas movies from these legendary quotes.

"This is the house I asked Kris for, and he got me a dad, and the third thing I'll just have to wait for."

____

"I am the Ghost of Christmas Past."

____

"What kind of hotel allows a child to check in alone?"

____

"Enough! Enough with this Turbo Man, okay? I have had it up to here with this Turbo Man! If there's anybody I don't want advice from right now, it's Turbo Man!"

____

"Patch gone? Where will he go? What will he do? The world is no place for an elf."

____

Christmas Sudoku 1

Fill in the blank squares so that each row, each column, and each 3-by-3 block contain the letters A, E, F, K, L, N, O, S, W.

Solve the puzzle and find the hidden word in the highlighted squares.

N			E		A	L	K	F
		L						A
					K			W
		E			S	K		
			O		N			
		F	K			O		
F			N					
E						A		
A	W	K	S		L			O

Cheeky Elf Whodunnit

Santa has a loyal but mischievous crew of elves who help him make toys each year. One day at the factory, Santa went to grab his lunch from the staff refrigerator and discovered that someone had taken a nibble out of his cheese sandwich.

After arguing for hours and missing their production targets, the elf police were called and interrogated the five prime suspects. Can you guess the guilty party if only three of the following statements are true?

1. **Alabaster Snowball: 'Bushy Evergreen did it.'**
2. **Pepper Minstix: 'It wasn't me.'**
3. **Shinny Upatree: 'Sugarplum Mary is innocent.'**
4. **Bushy Evergreen: 'Alabaster Snowball is lying when he accuses me.'**
5. **Sugarplum Mary: 'Pepper Minstix is telling the truth.'**

Answer: ______________________________

Turn to page 26

Spot the Difference

See how good you are at spotting the 6 subtle differences in these Christmas Eve fireplace scenes. Good luck!

Reindeer Search

The names of Santa's nine special reindeers are hidden below. Can you find and circle them?

X	B	Y	I	T	Z	O	B	N	R	E	X	K	N
Z	F	U	M	P	C	S	M	M	I	C	T	X	D
S	E	E	P	P	O	Z	B	P	R	A	E	L	O
G	B	O	E	N	N	W	J	O	P	J	F	X	N
D	Z	O	S	D	H	F	S	D	R	P	P	X	N
M	R	G	Q	J	O	I	A	K	A	Z	H	A	E
D	T	D	G	S	H	N	Z	L	N	C	N	Q	R
A	L	I	P	K	C	D	F	C	C	N	X	B	S
V	R	P	B	E	D	J	Q	A	E	S	P	K	L
M	W	U	R	P	S	E	H	Z	R	Z	W	L	B
X	D	C	D	L	O	T	T	C	E	X	G	U	Q
L	O	A	N	O	N	I	M	J	H	O	M	D	E
A	T	F	Q	T	L	E	F	Q	S	X	E	M	T
I	L	K	Y	B	M	P	X	J	A	K	H	E	V
N	A	D	C	I	L	V	H	I	D	J	M	P	X
W	K	Z	V	A	N	W	P	A	V	O	P	O	Y
O	V	H	U	L	H	S	Q	F	C	K	T	N	P

Connect the Dots

Connect the dots to reveal the picture. Use the numbers to guide you. When you land on a dot with a circle around it, take your pen off and start again at the next number with a star.

Christmas Sudoku 2

Fill in the blank squares so that each row, each column, and each 3-by-3 block contain the letters A, C, F, J, K, R, O, S, T.

Solve the puzzle and find the hidden word in the highlighted squares.

S					O	R	K	J
				J		F	A	
		J	A		K			
R		A				C		O
			T		C	A		
	J	R		K				
K	O	T	F					S

Past Popular Presents

These were all super popular toys that sold massively at Christmas in the year they were released. For each decade below, only one of the three toys were released in that decade. Circle it.

----------- 1980s -----------

Rubik's Cube

TMNT

Stretch Armstrong

----------- 1990s -----------

Gameboy

Simon

Tamagotchi

----------- 2000s -----------

Furby

Bratz

Build-A-Bear

Number Puzzle Picture

In any order you wish, copy the contents of each square in the jumbled picture below to the same numbered square in the blank grid on the next page until the entire puzzle is done, then add vivid Christmas shades to your masterpiece.

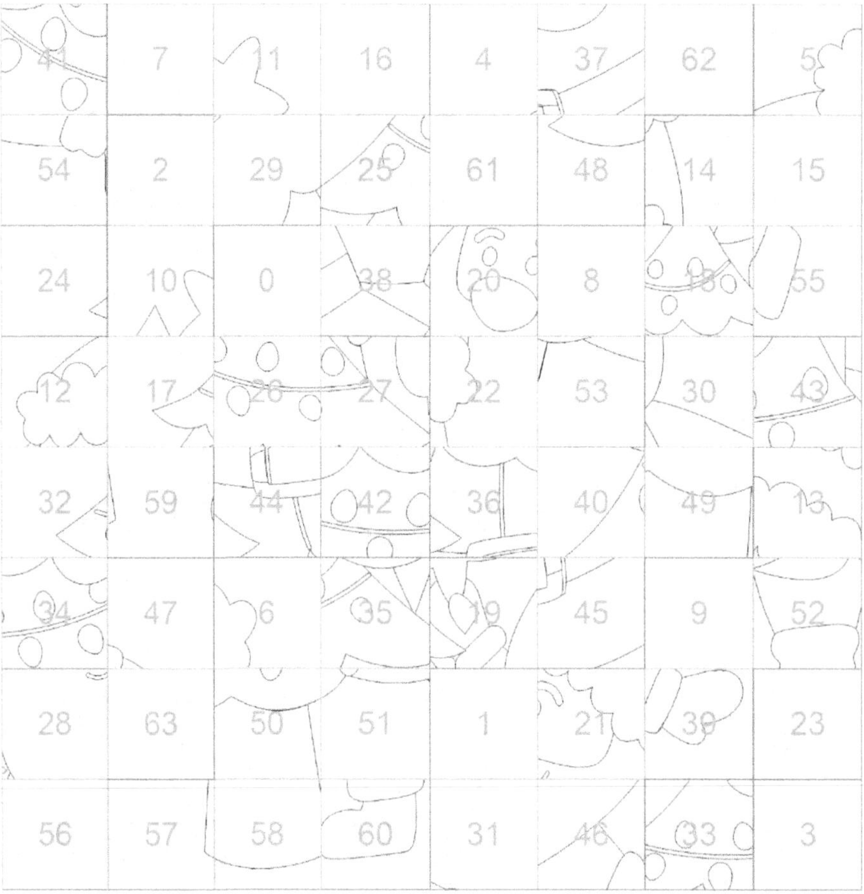

41	7	11	16	4	37	62	5
54	2	29	25	61	48	14	15
24	10	0	38	20	8	18	55
12	17	26	27	22	53	30	43
32	59	44	42	36	40	49	13
34	47	6	35	19	45	9	52
28	63	50	51	1	21	39	23
56	57	58	60	31	46	33	3

0	1	2	3	4	5	6	7
8	9	10	11	12	13	14	15
16	17	18	19	20	21	22	23
24	25	26	27	28	29	30	31
32	33	34	35	36	37	38	39
40	41	42	43	44	45	46	47
48	49	50	51	52	53	54	55
56	57	58	59	60	61	62	63

Name the Movie 2

Guess the classic Christmas movies from these legendary quotes.

"What is it you want, Mary? What do you want? You want the moon? Just say the word and I'll throw a lasso around it and pull it down."

____

"SANTA! OH MY GOD! SANTA'S COMING! I KNOW HIM! I KNOW HIM!"

____

"No, thank YOU. One thing about trains... it doesn't matter where they're going. What matters is deciding to get on."

____

"You want me to take the toys down the chimney into a strange house in my underwear!?"

____

"I made my family disappear."

____

Note Space

Use these pages if you need to jot something down when solving the puzzles and riddles in this section.

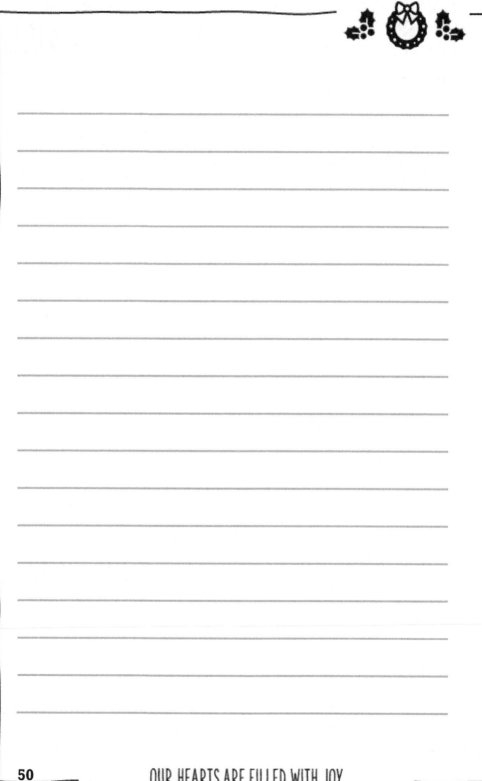

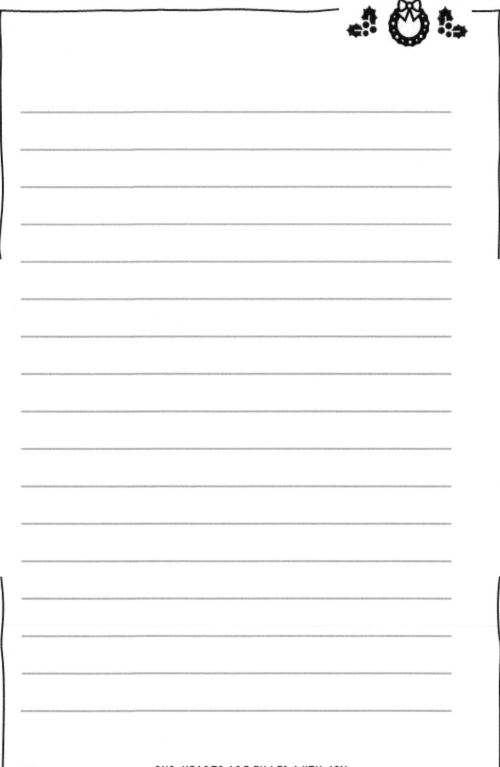

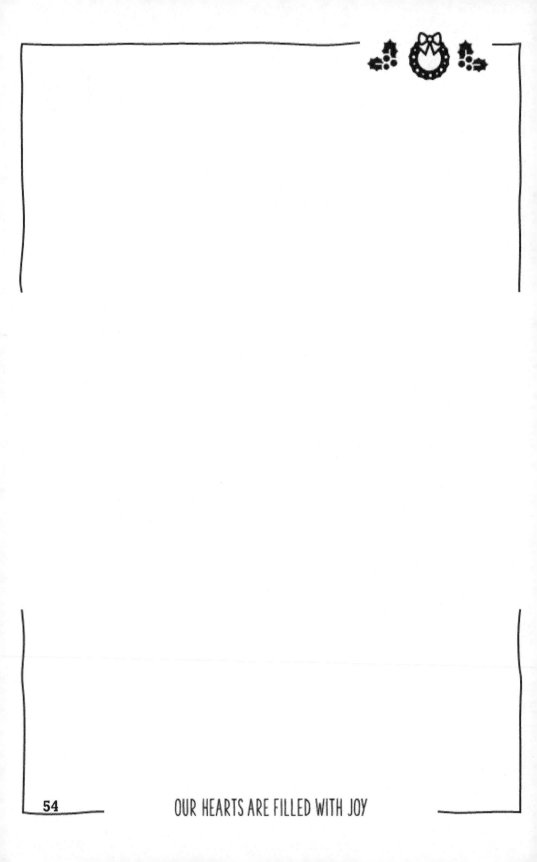

PART 3

THE ANSWERS

Let's see how well you did.

Mary and Joseph Meet

Mary and Joseph want to meet but are moving in opposite directions around the town. Mary moves two places counterclockwise at each stage and Joseph moves one place clockwise at each stage. After how many stages will they be together in the same corner of town?

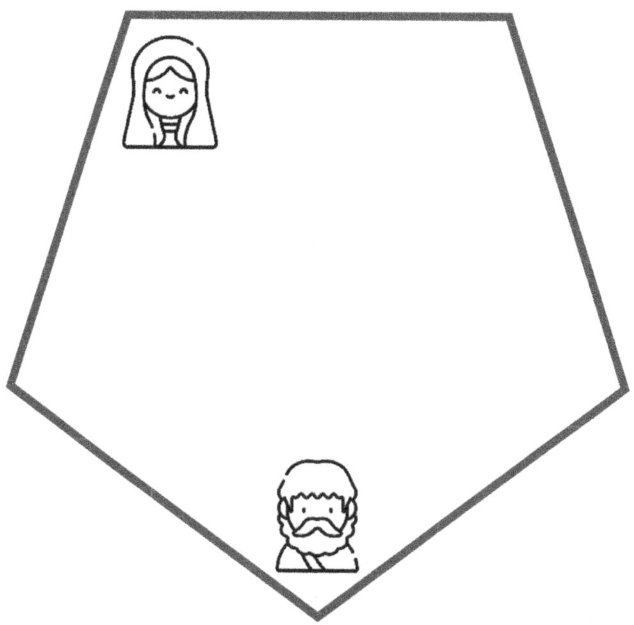

Answer:

B: After 4 Stages

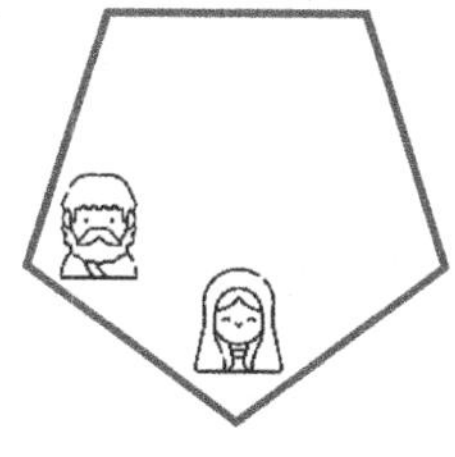

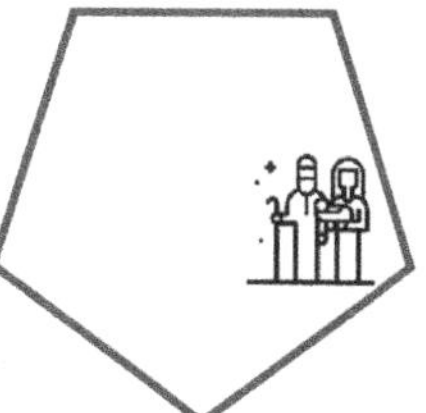

Noel Number Puzzle Picture

In any order you wish, copy the contents of each square in the jumbled picture below to the same numbered square in the blank grid on the next page until the entire puzzle is done, then add vivid shades to your masterpiece.

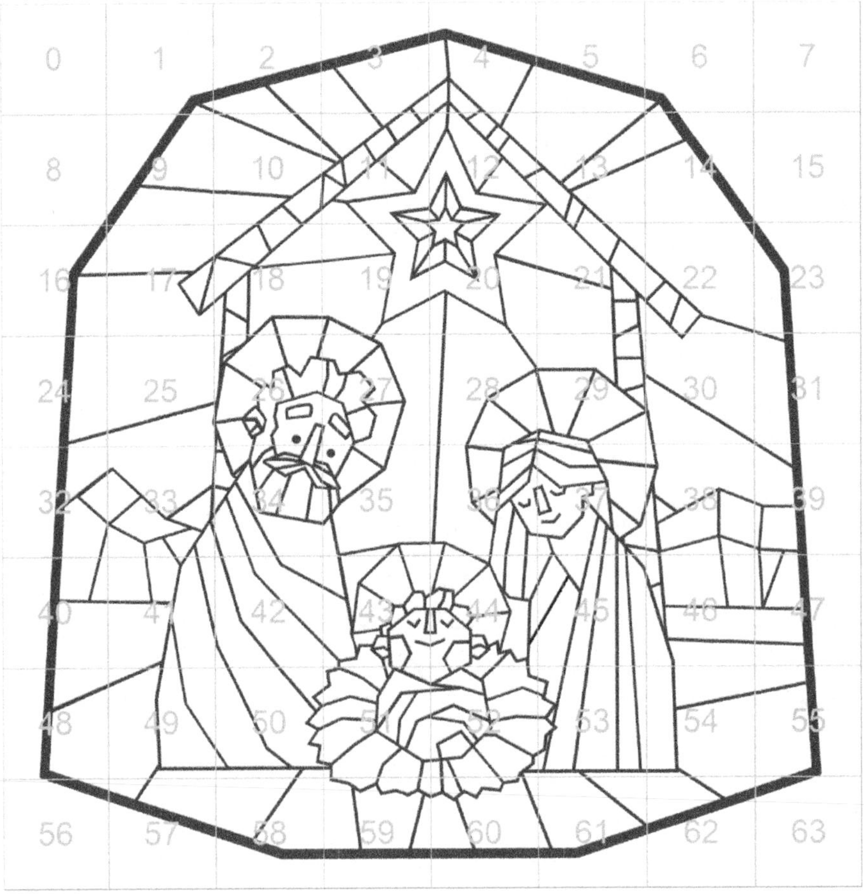

Carol Search

The titles of six traditional carols based on the Nativity are hidden below. Can you find and circle them?

M	X	B	V	J	H	W	Y	J	Q	C	M	U	T	V
C	C	G	L	U	P	H	B	O	G	F	X	G	N	Z
F	S	J	I	F	M	A	Y	H	B	Y	F	N	M	T
C	W	P	E	Z	Z	T	A	O	N	O	O	Q	Z	H
O	E	L	Y	A	Z	C	B	L	F	C	S	A	E	G
P	T	W	W	H	V	H	U	Y	O	B	E	F	F	I
M	H	V	N	L	H	I	Y	N	S	W	D	J	G	N
X	R	V	X	I	D	L	E	I	K	R	W	G	R	T
P	E	V	T	I	Z	D	O	G	D	E	A	F	J	N
F	E	I	R	P	T	I	P	H	G	A	M	A	L	E
B	K	C	N	L	J	S	P	T	E	N	V	U	L	L
M	I	E	I	V	I	T	Y	Q	W	T	M	A	C	I
D	N	J	N	T	K	H	R	K	M	W	C	Z	O	S
F	G	D	A	Y	N	I	H	M	Y	Z	Q	B	C	H
Y	S	G	H	D	U	S	K	G	J	Y	G	V	T	Z
F	R	E	G	N	A	M	A	N	I	Y	A	W	A	Q
V	P	H	O	S	B	W	T	J	Z	A	L	W	A	M
A	E	G	L	O	R	A	C	O	S	P	Y	L	A	C

Starring Role Riddler

Rearrange these phrases to reveal some unforgettable people from the Nativity story.

Faze no, just share

Answer: **Jesus of Nazareth**

Brighten mass delivery

Answer: **The Blessed Virgin Mary**

The red-hot rage

Answer: **Herod the Great**

Rut cause us saga

Answer: **Caesar Augustus**

Ruthless Sudoku

Fill in the blank squares so that each row, each column, and each 3-by-3 block contain the letters C, D, E, H, J, O, R, S, U.

The letters you produce from the highlighted squares completes the following phrase:

"I, King HERO<u>D</u> ordered all the male children under two years in Bethlehem to be killed in my attempt to get rid of the baby Jesus."

D	O	**C**	**R**	H	E	U	**S**	J
S	R	**H**	U	**J**	D	**C**	E	**O**
E	U	J	S	C	O	D	**H**	R
O	J	D	**E**	**S**	H	R	U	**C**
C	S	R	**D**	O	**U**	E	J	H
U	H	E	J	**R**	**C**	S	O	**D**
J	**C**	U	H	E	R	O	D	**S**
R	D	**S**	O	**U**	J	**H**	C	E
H	**E**	O	C	D	**S**	**J**	R	**U**

Wise Letters

Test your creative thinking skills with these challenging letter puzzles.

1. Which letter is three to the right of the letter immediately to the left of the letter that is four to the left of the letter O?

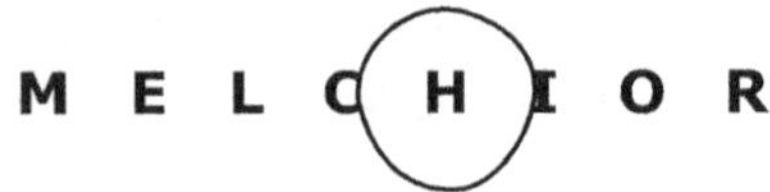

2. I am a 9-letter wise man.
9, 2, 7, 5 = being hasty
7, 6, 3, 4 = an essential seasoning
1, 8, 4 = used to hit baseballs
Who am I?
= BALTHASAR

3. What letter should replace the question mark in this star?
V. The letters spell the name "GASPAR"

Chronicle Crossword

							1 F							
				2 M	Y	R	R	H						
			3 M				A							
		4 C	A	R	P	E	N	T	E	R		5 L		
			N				K					U		
			G				I					K		
			E				6 N	A	Z	A	R	E	T	H
7 S	T	A	R				C							
					8 I		E							
		9 G			M		N							
		O			M		S							
	10 E	L	I	Z	A	B	E	T	H					
11 M		D			N									
A					U									
12 G	A	B	R	I	E	L								
I					L									

Star Sudoku

Fill in the blank squares so that each row, each column, and each 3-by-3 block contain the letters A, D, E, G, N, O, S, T, V.

The letters you produce from the highlighted squares completes the following phrase:

"_____________ is the season of reflection and preparation for the birth of Jesus Christ."

D	**E**	V	N	O	**T**	G	S	A
N	G	**O**	**S**	V	A	E	T	D
T	**S**	**A**	D	**G**	E	N	**O**	V
S	T	**G**	V	N	**O**	**A**	D	E
A	D	E	T	**S**	**G**	**O**	**V**	**N**
V	O	**N**	A	E	**D**	**S**	G	T
O	**A**	**T**	G	**D**	N	V	**E**	S
G	N	**S**	**E**	T	V	D	A	O
E	**V**	D	O	A	**S**	T	N	G

Complete the Carol Lyrics

Nothing beats singing traditional hymns at Christmas time. Fill in the blanks below with the correct lyrics and prove yourself a Christmas carol expert.

"O come, all ye faithful, joyful and triumphant,
Come ye, O come ye, to Bethlehem.
Come and behold Him, born the King of angels"

O Come, All Ye Faithful

"Children, go where I send thee
How shall I send thee?
I'm gonna send thee one by one
One for the little bitty baby
That was born, born
Born in Bethlehem"

Children, Go Where I Send Thee

"Joy to the world! the Lord is come
Let earth receive her King
Let every heart prepare Him room,
and heaven and nature sing"

Joy to the World

Manger Memory

Let's put your memory to the test. Which of the following four images matches exactly with the nativity scene image at the start of this book?

How Many Can You Spot?

How many candy canes are in this picture? **39**

Complete the Lyrics

The following lyrics were taken from classic Christmas songs you no doubt love listening to year after year. But your help is needed to fill in the missing words.

"It's the most wonderful time of the year
With the kids <u>jingle</u> <u>belling</u>
And everyone telling you be of <u>good</u> cheer
It's the most wonderful time of the year"

It's The Most Wonderful Time of The Year

"Jingle bell, jingle bell, jingle bell <u>rock</u>
Jingle bells swing and jingle bells ring
<u>Snowing</u> and <u>blowing</u> up bushels of fun
Now the jingle <u>hop</u> has begun"

Jingle Bell Rock

"I'm <u>dreaming</u> of a white Christmas
Just like the <u>ones</u> I used to know
Where the treetops <u>glisten</u>
And children listen
To hear <u>sleigh</u> <u>bells</u> in the snow"

White Christmas

"Rockin' around the Christmas tree

At the Christmas party hop

Mistletoe hung where you can see

Every couple tries to stop"

Rockin Around The Christmas Tree

"I saw Mommy kissing Santa Claus

Underneath the mistletoe last night

She didn't see me creep

Down the stairs to have a peep"

I Saw Mommy Kissing Santa Claus

"Have yourself a merry little Christmas

Let your heart be light

From now on your troubles will be out of sight"

Have Yourself a Merry Little Christmas

"I don't want a lot for Christmas

There is just one thing I need

I don't care about the presents underneath the Christmas tree"

All I Want for Christmas is You

The Twelve Days Crossword

Test your knowledge of 'The Twelve Days of Christmas' – the classic, singalong Christmas carol that runs through the twelve days that make up the Christmas season from Christmas Day and to 6 January, the day before Epiphany.

								1 F								
								I					2 D			
								V					A			
								3 E	L	E	V	E	N			
							4 A						C			
							L			5 T		6 E	I	G	H	T
							E			U			N			
			7 C			8 P	A	R	T	R	I	D	G	E		
			A				P			T						
			L				I			L						
		9 A	L	A	Y	I	N	G		E						
			I				G			D						
10 F	R	E	N	C	H			11 S		O						
			G			12 T	W	E	L	V	E					
								V		E						
								E		S						
								N								

THE MAGIC OF CHRISTMAS IS NOT IN THE PRESENTS

Delicious Dessert

Nothing brings back memories like the sweets of a childhood Christmas. See if you can guess the popular Yuletide dessert from just the ingredients below...without feeling hungry!

Eggs
Golden caster sugar
Plain flour
Cocoa powder
Baking powder
Butter
Dark chocolate
Golden syrup
Double cream
Icing sugar
Holly sprigs to decorate

Answer: Chocolate Yule Log

CLUE: This dessert is best suited to be eaten by the fireplace. The filling sometimes includes crushed mints, but it's the original that will surely take your tastebuds on a trip down memory lane.

Name the Movie 1

Guess the classic Christmas movies from these legendary quotes.

"This is the house I asked Kris for, and he got me a dad, and the third thing I'll just have to wait for."

Miracle on 34th Street

"I am the Ghost of Christmas Past."

Scrooge

"What kind of hotel allows a child to check in alone?"

Home Alone 2: Lost in New York

"Enough! Enough with this Turbo Man, okay? I have had it up to here with this Turbo Man! If there's anybody I don't want advice from right now, it's Turbo Man!"

Jingle All The Way

"Patch gone? Where will he go? What will he do? The world is no place for an elf."

Santa Claus: The Movie

Turn to page 87

Christmas Sudoku 1

Fill in the blank squares so that each row, each column, and each 3-by-3 block contain the letters A, E, F, K, L, N, O, S, W.

Solve the puzzle and find the hidden word in the highlighted squares.

N	O	W	**E**	S	**A**	**L**	**K**	**F**
K	E	**L**	W	N	F	S	O	**A**
S	F	A	L	O	**K**	N	E	**W**
O	N	**E**	A	W	**S**	**K**	F	L
L	K	S	**O**	F	**N**	W	A	E
W	A	**F**	**K**	L	E	**O**	S	N
F	S	O	**N**	A	W	E	L	K
E	L	N	F	K	O	**A**	W	S
A	**W**	**K**	**S**	E	**L**	F	N	**O**

Cheeky Elf Whodunnit

Santa has a loyal but mischievous crew of elves who help him make toys each year. One day at the factory, Santa went to grab his lunch from the staff refrigerator and discovered that someone had taken a nibble out of his cheese sandwich.

After interrogating the five prime suspects for hours, Santa still couldn't work out who'd done it. Can you guess the guilty party if only three of the following statements are true?

1. Alabaster Snowball: 'Bushy Evergreen did it.'
2. Pepper Minstix: 'It wasn't me.'
3. Shinny Upatree: 'Sugarplum Mary is innocent.'
4. Bushy Evergreen: 'Alabaster Snowball is lying when he accuses me.'
5. Sugarplum Mary: 'Pepper Minstix is telling the truth.'

Sugarplum Mary did it! Check the statements in the table below and notice only Sugarplum Mary has three ticks against her name, meaning that the three statements given by Pepper Minstix, Bushy Evergreen, and Sugarplum Mary were true.

	Statements				
Culprit	Alabaster Snowball	Pepper Minstix	Shinny Upatree	Bushy Evergreen	Sugarplum Mary
Alabaster Snowball		√	√	√	√
Pepper Minstix			√	√	
Shinny Upatree		√	√	√	√
Bushy Evergreen	√	√	√		√
Sugarplum Mary		√		√	√

Spot the Difference

See how good you are at spotting the 6 subtle differences in these Christmas Eve fireplace scenes. Good luck!

Reindeer Search

The names of Santa's nine special reindeers are hidden below. Can you find and circle them?

X	B	Y	I	T	Z	O	B	N	R	E	X	K	N
Z	F	U	M	P	C	S	M	M	I	C	T	X	D
S	E	E	P	P	O	Z	B	P	R	A	E	L	O
G	B	O	E	N	N	W	J	O	P	J	F	X	N
D	Z	O	S	D	H	F	S	D	R	P	P	X	N
M	R	G	Q	J	O	I	A	K	A	Z	H	A	E
D	T	D	G	S	H	N	Z	L	N	C	N	Q	R
A	L	I	P	K	C	D	F	C	C	N	X	B	S
V	R	P	B	E	D	J	Q	A	E	S	P	K	L
M	W	U	R	P	S	E	H	Z	R	Z	W	L	B
X	D	C	D	L	O	T	T	C	E	X	G	U	Q
L	O	A	N	O	N	I	M	J	H	O	M	D	E
A	T	F	Q	T	L	E	F	Q	S	X	E	M	T
I	L	K	Y	B	M	P	X	J	A	K	H	E	V
N	A	D	C	I	L	V	H	I	D	J	M	P	X
W	K	Z	V	A	N	W	P	A	V	O	P	O	Y
O	V	H	U	L	H	S	Q	F	C	K	T	N	P

Christmas Sudoku 2

Fill in the blank squares so that each row, each column, and each 3-by-3 block contain the letters A, C, F, J, K, R, O, S, T.

Solve the puzzle and find the hidden word in the highlighted squares.

S	T	F	C	A	**O**	**R**	**K**	**J**
O	R	K	S	**J**	T	**F**	**A**	C
J	A	C	K	F	R	O	S	T
T	C	**J**	**A**	O	**K**	S	F	R
R	K	**A**	J	S	F	**C**	T	**O**
F	S	O	**T**	R	**C**	**A**	J	K
C	F	S	R	T	J	K	O	A
A	**J**	**R**	O	**K**	S	T	C	F
K	**O**	**T**	**F**	C	A	J	R	**S**

Past Popular Presents

These were all super popular toys that sold massively at Christmas in the year they were released. For each decade below, only one of the three toys were released in that decade. Circle it.

1980s

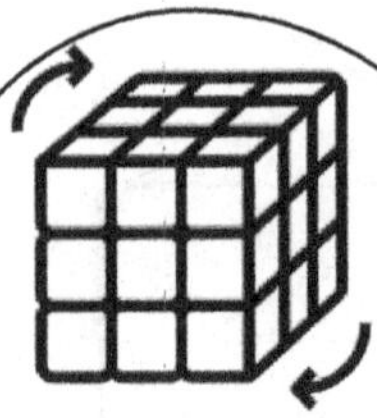

Rubik's Cube  TMNT  Stretch Armstrong

1990s

Gameboy  Simon  Tamagotchi

2000s

Furby  Bratz  Build-A-Bear

Number Puzzle Picture

In any order you wish, copy the contents of each square in the jumbled picture below to the same numbered square in the blank grid on the next page until the entire puzzle is done, then add vivid Christmas shades to your masterpiece.

0	1	2	3	4	5	6	7
8	9	10	11	12	13	14	15
16	17	18	19	20	21	22	23
24	25	26	27	28	29	30	31
32	33	34	35	36	37	38	39
40	41	42	43	44	45	46	47
48	49	50	51	52	53	54	55
56	57	58	59	60	61	62	63

Name the Movie 2

Guess the classic Christmas movies from these legendary quotes.

"What is it you want, Mary? What do you want? You want the moon? Just say the word and I'll throw a lasso around it and pull it down.

It's a Wonderful Life

"SANTA! OH MY GOD! SANTA'S COMING! I KNOW HIM! I KNOW HIM!"

Elf

"No, thank YOU. One thing about trains... it doesn't matter where they're going. What matters is deciding to get on."

The Polar Express

"You want me to take the toys down the chimney into a strange house in my underwear!?"

The Santa Clause

"I made my family disappear."

Home Alone

THE MAGIC OF CHRISTMAS IS NOT IN THE PRESENTS

BONUS: Badge

To make your Christmas even more special, here is an exquisite badge for you to cut out and wear with PRIDE.

Go on... spread your Christmas cheer with those you love!

BE MERRY and JOYFUL

More From JEST FEST

I sincerely hope this book brought you lots of Christmas cheer. If you're still in the puzzle mood, or looking for a fun gift, I've got you covered.

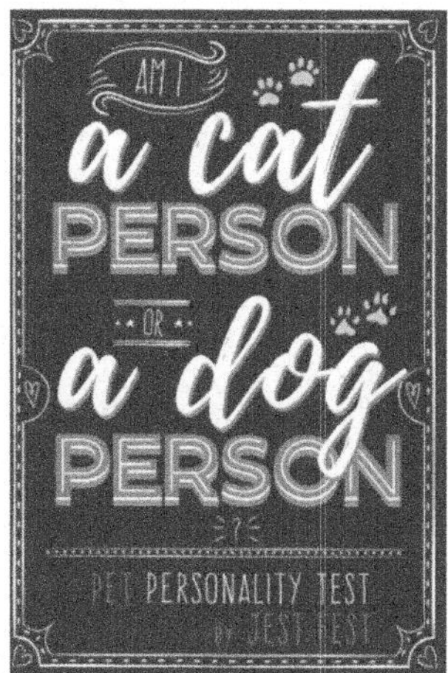

MERRY CHRISTMAS

HAVE A WONDERFUL TIME WITH YOUR LOVED ONES AND A SPECIAL NEW YEAR!

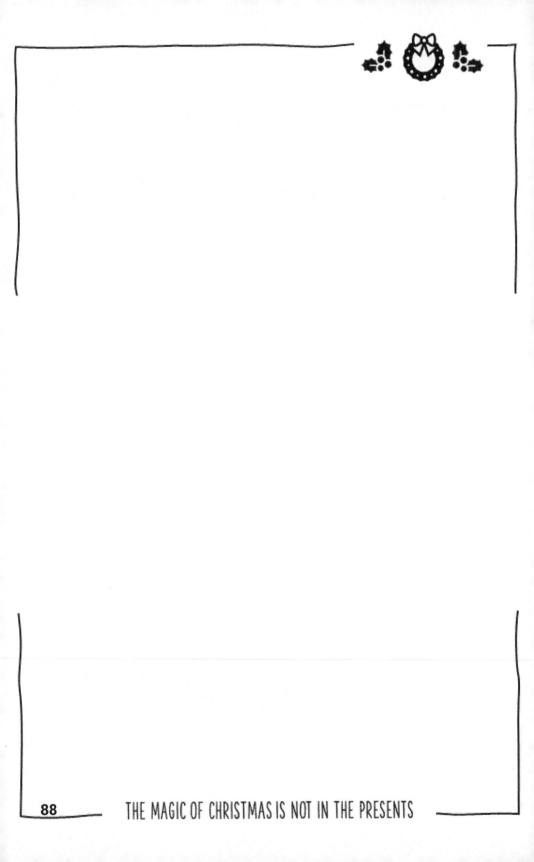

Extraordinary Christmases

Largest Gathering of People Wearing Santa Hats

The largest gathering of people wearing Santa hats is 30,333 and was achieved by Angels Baseball (USA) at Angel Stadium in Anaheim, California, USA, on 25 June 2014.

Christmas Day Babies

Christmas Day ranks among the least popular birthdays worldwide, except in places surrounding the equator like El Salvador, where the most common baby name is Maria (Mary). Ironically, babies conceived on Christmas Day have one of the top four most common birthday dates (September 17).

The Gospel According to Luke

The words "all" and "entire" are used 23 times in Luke 1-2, highlighting the universal scope of God's offer of salvation through Christ and the massive number of mighty acts God performed surrounding His birth.

Why Decorate Evergreen Trees

Evergreen trees were the symbol of eternal life. Martin Luther introduced them to the Reformation Church as a picture of our endless life in Christ, by bringing in a tree to his family on Christmas Eve lit with candles.

Tallest Chocolate Father Christmas

The tallest chocolate Father Christmas (hollow) measured 5 m (16 ft 4.85 in) and was achieved by the shopping centre Mirabello (Italy) in Cantù, Italy, on 11 December 2011.

Dreaming of a White Christmas

In the town of North Pole, Alaska, there's a 100 percent chance of snow on the ground on Christmas morning, and visitors to this aptly named town can expect to wake to an average of 12 inches. It's also known for its year-round Christmas decorations, including candy cane–striped streetlights.

Pickle Tree Decoration

Most likely a German Christmas tradition, but now practiced by many people around the world, this tradition sees families hang a pickle-like ornament on their Christmas trees. It’s popular among families with young children and the first child that finds it gets a gift along with tons of luck for the next year.

The Silent Father

The Bible does not record a single word spoken by Joseph. Some have quipped that he is always asleep when pictured in the Bible, since Matthew twice records an angel appearing to him in a dream.

Largest Display of Knitted Christmas Decorations
The largest display of knitted Christmas decorations consists of 8,845 decorations and was achieved by Woman's Weekly (UK), in London, UK, on 2 September 2014.

The Gospel According to Matthew
A star was not the only guide the magi had in finding the baby Jesus. Matthew says the star guided then as far as Jerusalem, where they learned that Scripture foretold the Jewish Messiah's birth in Bethlehem.

But the best Christmas event of all? ... Jesus was born!

Made in the USA
Las Vegas, NV
23 November 2022